MW00826529

Mother and Daughter

A Record Book

Tenderness

Joy

Hope

Happiness

Laughter

Reflections of a
Lifetime of Love

© 2001 Havoc Publishing
San Diego, California
U.S.A.
Text © Kathy Cisneros

ISBN 0-7416-1919-9

All rights reserved.
No part of this publication may be reproduced or
transmitted in any form or by any means, electronic or
mechanical, including photocopying, recording, any
information storage and retrieval system without
permission in writing from the publisher.

www.havocpub.com

Made in Korea

This record book reflects
the love shared in the lives of:
_____ and _____

*I*t only took a moment

for my life to change

forever.

Earliest Memories

Mother to Daughter

The first time I looked into your eyes, I felt: _____

_____

_____

The first time I held you in my arms, I held you in my heart for the rest of my life. I knew at that moment I would

always remember: _____

_____

_____

My instincts were to shelter and protect you from the world. The first time you cried on the night I brought you

home, I remember thinking: _____

_____

_____

As you lay in your cradle content in your dreams, I was fulfilled in watching you sleep. My prayer for you to the

Angels was:_____

_____

Daughter to Mother

My earliest memories of your love built the foundation on which I now stand. My earliest memories of your face

were:_____

_____

Even before my mouth could form the words my heart was feeling, we communicated through expression with a

language uniquely our own. Even now, the sound of your voice makes me feel: _____

_____

Earliest Memories

Mother to Daughter

In choosing your name, I chose carefully. The reason I chose _____ for you was:_____

_____

_____

I read all the books and heard all the advice on raising a daughter. The wisdom I gained was:_____

_____

_____

_____

The sound of your laughter was all I lived for. The toy that brought you the most smiles was:_____

_____

_____

_____

I remember when I was your age. The toy I cherished the most was:_____

_____

_____

_____

At first there were precious moments of silence. They were only enhanced when you spoke your first words. Your

first words were:_____

_____

Your eyes were full of excitement and achievement as you gingerly took your first steps. You walked for the

first time on:_____

_____

The sound

of your laughter

brought me great joy.

I remember the music

we sang together.

Preferences

Daughter to Mother

I learned of your favorite music through lullabies. The song I remember most is:_____

_____

_____

_____

_____

You calm my fears with your special touch by: _____

_____

_____

_____

_____

The scent that filters through my mind and always takes me home is: _____

_____

_____

_____

_____

Even though you tried your best to make me like it, I could never get used to the taste of:_____

_____

_____

_____

_____

The day you were born,

Your tiny hands reached for that

Place in my heart

That brought out the best within me.

You looked to me to

fill all of your needs.

$\mathcal{D}$eep inside me I knew,

The best I could do,

Was to teach you the skills to be free.

You'll carry my love in your smile,

A true reflection of me.

I wanted to reach out and catch you each time you fell.

Endeavors

Mother to Daughter

I remember the first time you were hurt was when: _____

_____

_____

I wanted to reach out and catch you each time you fell. The time I was unable to was: _____

_____

_____

_____

One hard lesson you learned at an early age was: _____

_____

_____

_____

I remember thinking how much my instruction to you was a reflection of my own experiences. I remember

telling you: _____

_____

_____

_____

_____

_____

_____

_____

Memories

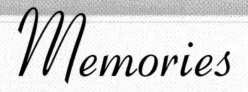

Daughter to Mother

You had ways of making the simplest foods delicious. My favorite was:_____
_____
_____
_____
_____
_____

It seemed no matter how hard I tried, I could never master that recipe you cooked so well. Only you could make:_____
_____
_____
_____
_____
_____
_____
_____

I have memories of your kitchen filled with the aroma of baking. Some of my favorite sweets were:_____
_____

*B*aking was a treat

we both enjoyed.

I remember

your colorful

world of crayons.

A Small Child

Mother to Daughter

The first picture you drew for me was: _____

_____

_____

Your toys were treasures you could not be without. However, in time you grew out of: _____

_____

_____

Daughter to Mother

I remember colorful carnival lights and the motions of merry-go-rounds as they swirled through my mind. My

favorite ride was: _____

_____

_____

I recall the walls and mountains of books at the library. My favorite book was: _____

_____

_____

The days spent at the playground flow through my mind as sweet memories. You were then my best friend and I

watched you become like a little girl again as we played: _____

_____

_____

_____

Place photograph here

For all of the things you taught me in life,

For all of my dreams that came true,

My life would mean nothing at all,

If not for the love that we knew.

You never knew how
I hid my fears when
you had your first day of school.

School

Mother to Daughter

It's hard to release your cherished child into the unknown world of life. Your first day of school went like this:_____

_____

_____

In breaking away from these hours with you, I was learning in spurts to let you go. I remember one time you left

home without me: _____

_____

_____

You would come home with new ideas and songs and I had to adjust to the world that touched your mind. You were

so excited the first time you told me about:_____

_____

_____

I encouraged your thirst to learn as you grew. I remember you were so excited to learn about: _____

_____

_____

Daughter to Mother

On that first day of school I felt my heart pounding. I tried to be brave as you waved goodbye. I remember thinking:

_____

_____

My teacher wasn't my mother but nurtured me in your absence. The name of my favorite teacher was_____

I'll never forget my teacher because:_____

Birthdays

Daughter to Mother

One birthday that stands out in my mind was:_____

_____

_____

_____

_____

Mother to Daughter

I loved preparing your parties and finding that one present you always wished for the most. One birthday, you

wished for:_____

_____

_____

_____

_____

I'll never forget the look on your face when one year I surprised you by having your party at:_____

_____

_____

_____

_____

_____

I celebrated each birthday watching the changes taking place deep inside you.

Love

Mother to Daughter

It has been a pleasure being your mother. You changed me forever by:_____

_____

_____

_____

_____

Watching you and seeing how much you are like me, makes me appreciate as well how much you are not like me.

The way we share a beautiful difference is:_____

_____

_____

_____

You may have carried some of my physical traits but it's the way we share expressions that amazes me most. We

always:_____

_____

_____

_____

So many times when I looked at you, I saw myself in your eyes. I never told you that:_____

_____

_____

_____

_____

You enriched my life

in so many ways.

You touched each holiday

in your own unique way,

making each one special

for me
to live through
and look back on.

Holidays

Mother to Daughter

I wanted to give you the joys of what I remembered from my childhood holidays. The holiday I enjoyed the most

with you will always be: _____

_____

Ever since you were small, you found ways to make my Mother's Day special. The one that I remember most is

when you: _____

_____

If they had invented such a thing as a Daughter's Day, I would have celebrated yours by: _____

_____

Daughter to Mother

My favorite holiday that we shared will always be: _____

_____

_____

_____

You and I spent hours choosing a Halloween costume for me to wear! The best costume we ever came up with

was: _____

_____

_____

You taught me the true meaning of giving each holiday. I remember the moment when I was more excited to

give than to receive was _____

_____

_____

Place photograph here

Wherever you go,

deep inside you will know,

You'll carry

my love in your smile.

You no longer believed

in the tooth fairy

and you hardly
ever touched your crayons.

Teen Years

Mother to Daughter

I remember having to tolerate your music with a smile. Do you remember the group you were wild about?_____

_____

I remember the meals you refused to eat because of some trend you just had to try. Once I remember the only thing

you would eat was _____ and I felt:_____

_____

_____

As I folded your clothes and put them away, I thought of how fashions had come full circle. Do you remember how

you wouldn't be caught dead in front of your friends without wearing:_____

_____

I never thought I'd see the day when you wouldn't let me kiss you in front of your friends. It hurt but I understood

when you said: _____

Daughter to Mother

I was still a little girl but I was changing. I still needed your hugs and your kisses (just not in front of my friends). I

just didn't want them to think:_____

_____

You kept up with the music and trends of my generation but your rules were burdensome at times. I understand

now why you wouldn't let me:_____

_____

All my friends wanted you for their mother. You made everyone feel welcome in our home. One of my friends said:

_____

_____

Emotions

Mother to Daughter

You always knew no matter how bad it was, you could tell me. You were never afraid to be honest with me because

I could read your eyes. Once you told me:_____

_____

_____

I was so angry at the world when it hurt you. I wanted to run to your defense but you had to learn to fight your own

battles. One particular battle you fought was when:_____

_____

_____

Your first crush was one that affected you deeply. I remember how it went:_____

_____

Daughter to Mother

When that boy never called, you let me cry on your shoulder. I remember you saying:_____

_____

_____

_____

When we argued, it was devastating to me. One major argument we had involved:_____

_____

_____

_____

_____

_____

When that boy

never called,

you let me cry

on your

shoulder.

Deep inside me I knew

the best I could do

was to teach you

the skills to be free.

Place photograph here

Letting Go

Mother to Daughter

As a small child, you once told me you wanted to be a:_____

_____

_____

_____

One moment I was tying your shoes and the next you were moving out on your own . How did it happen so

quickly? I remember feeling:_____

_____

_____

I knew you would excel in your chosen field because:_____

_____

Daughter to Mother

I was filled with exuberant dreams of the future. I was scared and yet confident you would always be there to help

me as I stepped out into the world on my own. I remember thinking:_____

_____

_____

As I turned to leave you on that doorstep where my whole life had begun, tears filled my eyes and my heart sank,

knowing I was leaving you behind me. Yet I knew you would be with me in every sense of the word because:_____

_____

_____

_____

_____

We talked

over coffee

about your career plans.

Each time you came home to visit

was never long

enough for me.

Never Far Away

Mother to Daughter

At times, I think we spoke more when you were gone than when you were here. I remember wishing I had spent

more time:_____

_____

_____

I know I gave you more advice than you wanted. I wanted you to be safe in the world without me. I was so afraid of:

_____

Each time you came home to visit, it was never long enough for me. Unexpectedly, I found myself seeking your

approval. I knew you had matured when:_____

_____

_____

Daughter to Mother

How different it was not to come home to a bed that was made. The weight of the world rested on my decisions

now. My mind drifted back to when:_____

_____

_____

As I became more aware of the responsibilities I had to face on my own, I wondered where that smile came from

that you always had on your face. How did you ever manage to:_____

_____

_____

_____

_____

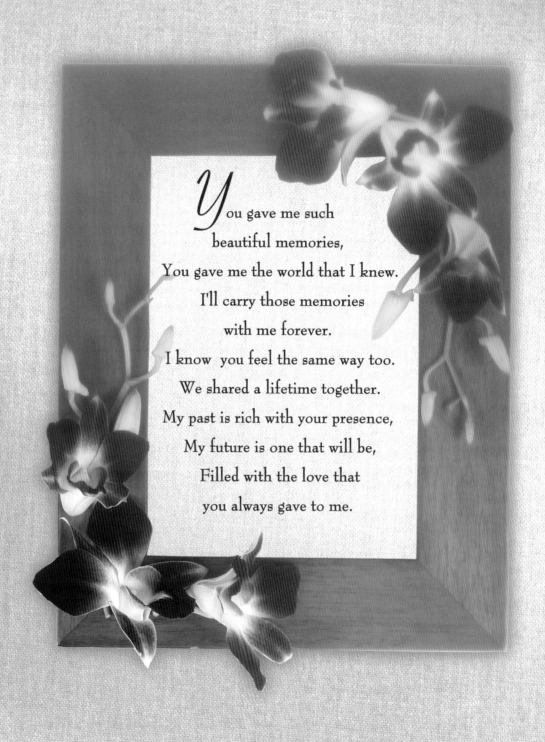

$\mathcal{Y}$ou gave me such
beautiful memories,
You gave me the world that I knew.
I'll carry those memories
with me forever.
I know you feel the same way too.
We shared a lifetime together.
My past is rich with your presence,
My future is one that will be,
Filled with the love that
you always gave to me.

Mothers and Daughters
are timeless.
Nothing will tear at the bond,
that brings us so close together,
in our dreams, in this life and beyond.
Keep us forever on pages,
in stages of all we went through.
Know in your heart all my feelings,
read how I simply love you.

Watch me grow and
then you'll know
what a person you made of me.

Place photograph here

It was important to teach you to be strong without me.

Reflections

Mother to Daughter

It was important to teach you how to get back on your feet after a disappointment. You were so disappointed when:

_____

_____

_____

I know you forever as no one else ever could. Once you tried to hide your feelings about:_____

_____

I learned more from you about myself than all of the world ever taught me. One of the greatest things I learned

from you was:_____

_____

_____

Daughter to Mother

Your approval and acceptance of the person I was learning to be, was all I ever needed to flourish. I remember being

so proud of myself when:_____

_____

_____

You influenced the person I am today by:_____

_____

_____

_____

_____

I will never

lock you out of my life.

Reflections

Mother to Daughter

I realized the impact I had on your life as an adult when you told me:_____

_____

_____

_____

_____

I was never trained in the art of being a mother. I improvised as I took hold of each challenge that faced me. One

of my most challenging moments was:_____

_____

_____

Every mother wishes to give her daughter the things she never had in her own life. My greatest wish was to give you:

_____

_____

_____

The ways I kept an opened mind to the decisions you made that I might not have agreed with:_____

_____

_____

_____

I am a reflection of
the mirror of your love

Reflections

Daughter to Mother

I remember saying prayers in my head at night. My prayer was:_____

_____

_____

_____

_____

I will always hear your words to me whenever I think of:_____

_____

_____

_____

I just can't imagine the world without you in it. I hope you realize:_____

_____

_____

_____

When I pick up a phone to call you, you always tell me:_____

_____

_____

_____

We're still there for each other,
as we journey apart,

but our love grows deeper,
for we're bound heart to heart.

Place photograph here

The Circle of Love

Mother to Daughter

So many times I heard my own mother's voice speaking through me. One of the things she said to me that I found myself saying to you was: _____

_____

_____

_____

_____

_____

You remind me of my mother in these ways: _____

_____

_____

_____

_____

_____

_____

To me, being your mother means: _____

_____

_____

_____

_____

_____

_____

The Circle of Love

Daughter to Mother

Yours was the shoulder I searched for to cry on, when no one else in the world would ever understand my tears. I

remember crying when I told you:_____

_____

_____

You made me feel precious and needed and loved. The time you made me feel my worth was when: _____

_____

_____

_____

_____

I loved to watch you from afar. Your poise and demeanor impressed me. I can remember the time when you:_____

_____

_____

_____

Your touch was a great comfort to me. I remember how you held my hand when we: _____

_____

_____

_____

Flipping through scrapbooks

of my grandmother's past,

I learn of her story through

bits and pieces

that will forever last.

Generations

Mother to Daughter

Having a daughter made me see my own mother as I had never seen her before. Thoughts of how she loved me made me remember: _____

_____

_____

When I was small I savored the stories my mother would tell me of her childhood. One story I loved hearing was about: _____

_____

_____

I find it truly amazing how each mother influences her future generations. I realized the impact my own grandmother had on my life by the way she: _____

_____

_____

Daughter to Mother

I remember feeling connected to my grandmother's spirit when I learned of: _____

_____

_____

There was always so much love in my grandmother's eyes. The kindest thing I remember her doing for someone was when she: _____

_____

_____

You gave me such
beautiful memories,
You gave me the world
that I knew.

Place photograph here

The greatest gift
I ever received
was having you
for a mother.

Love

Daughter to Mother

You were and always will be my best friend. I will always need you for:_____

_____

_____

_____

_____

I'm so glad it was you who brought me into the world. I saw the world through your eyes and kept the reflections in

my heart. For me, you will always be:_____

_____

_____

_____

_____

There is no greater bond than the love that is shared between a mother and a daughter. I will always feel:_____

_____

_____

_____

_____

Getting stronger, forever,

Just me and you.

Place photograph here

It makes me laugh
when I remember how much
you complained about my cooking.

Now you're constantly on the phone
asking for recipes to save the day.

Connections

Mother to Daughter

Here's a recipe you've always wanted:_____

_____

_____

_____

_____

When you were sick, I was always able to make you feel better by giving you:_____

_____

_____

_____

_____

Cleaning is a chore. The best trick for household cleaning I ever learned was: _____

_____

_____

Daughter to Mother

I was paying attention all those years you thought I ignored you! I even improved on one of your recipes by:_____

_____

_____

_____

_____

_____

_____

For Tomorrow

Mother to Daughter

Let's go forth into tomorrow as bonded as we've been in the past. Let's make a pact to always:_____

_____

_____

_____

Let me learn from you always. Teach me of your world and your life as you face the future. Build on the foundation

we've made with our lives by always sharing your:_____

_____

_____

I will never let go of the love we share:_____

_____

Daughter to Mother

Although I'm all grown up, I still need you. Sometimes I think I need you even more now because:_____

_____

_____

_____

I will never let go of the love we share: _____

_____

_____

I love you forever because:_____

_____

_____